WORKBOOK 1

English
No Problem!

Trish Kerns
Old Marshall Adult Education Center
Sacramento City Unified School District, CA

Patty Long
Old Marshall Adult Education Center
Sacramento City Unified School District, CA

New Readers Press

English—No Problem!™
English—No Problem! Workbook 1
ISBN 1-56420-361-1

Copyright © 2004 New Readers Press
New Readers Press
Division of ProLiteracy Worldwide
1320 Jamesville Avenue, Syracuse, New York 13210
www.newreaderspress.com

Printed in the United States of America
9   8   7   6   5   4   3   2   1

All proceeds from the sale of New Readers Press materials
support literacy programs in the United States and worldwide.

Acquisitions Editor: Paula L. Schlusberg
Developer: Mendoza and Associates
Project Director: Roseanne Mendoza
Project Editor: Pat Harrington-Wydell
Content Editor: Terrie Lipke
Production Director: Heather Witt-Badoud
Designer: Kimbrly Koennecke
Illustrations: Carolyn Boehmer, Matt Terry, Brian Wallace, James Wallace
Production Specialist: Jeffrey R. Smith
Cover Design: Kimbrly Koennecke
Photo Credits: Hal Silverman Studio
Cover Photography: Robert Mescavage Photography

Contents

Lesson 1 I'm Lost! I'm Late!

Exercise A Write the days of the week in order.

| Thursday |
| ✔ Sunday |
| Tuesday |
| Saturday |
| Monday |
| Friday |
| Wednesday |

1. _____Sunday_____

2. _____

3. _____

4. _____

5. _____

6. _____

7. _____

Exercise B Match the picture to the words.

a.   b.   c.   d.   e.

__e__ **1.** take a train

____ **2.** walk

____ **3.** drive a car

____ **4.** take a bus

____ **5.** ride a bike

One Step Up
How do you go places? Write sentences.

I take a bus to work.

Exercise C Write the correct word.

am	is	are	✔is	are

1. Tomas _____ is _____ lost.

2. Gary and Tomas _____ late.

3. Yelena and you _____ students.

4. I _____ early.

5. Gina _____ on time.

Exercise D How is the weather? Write sentences.

Monday	Tuesday	Wednesday	Thursday	Friday
sunny	sunny	cloudy	rainy	rainy

1. _It's sunny on Monday and Tuesday._____

2. _____

3. _____

Exercise E Write sentences about the picture.

cloudy	✔Friday	It's	on time

Friday 8:25

1. It's _____ Friday _____ .

2. _____ 8:25.

3. It is _____ .

4. Gary is _____ for school.

Lesson 2 Welcome!

Exercise A Underline the syllable that has the stress. Write the word.

1. <u>ci</u> ty   _____city_____

4. an swer   _____

2. sup plies   _____

5. o pen   _____

3. rain y   _____

6. Mon day   _____

Exercise B Write the words in the sentences.

✔Her	His	Her	Their

1. _____Her_____ zip code is 95432.

2. _____ phone number is 555-7835.

3. _____ address is 2354 Main Street.

4. _____ area code is 234.

Exercise C Answer the questions for you. Write sentences.

1. What is your name? _My name is_ _____.

2. What is your area code? _____

3. What is your phone number? _____

4. What is your city? _____

5. What is your state? _____

Exercise D Write the words in the puzzle.

Across

open
spell
tell
✔write

Down

ask
be
do
listen
✔raise
talk

Exercise E Write the words from Exercise D in the sentences. Use all the words. Remember to start each sentence with an uppercase letter.

1. _____Ask_____ your partner a question.

2. _____ your hand.

3. _____ your books.

4. _____ the answers in your notebook.

5. _____ about the answers.

6. _____ to your partner.

7. _____ Exercise A with your partner.

8. _____ me your name.

9. _____ your last name please.

10. _____ on time.

Lesson 3 Money for School!

Exercise A   Find the words. Look across ➔ and down ↓.
Circle the words. Write the words in your notebook.

| ask | ✔book | dictionary | money | pencils | pens |

```
l   m   f   i   n   k   d   i   b   n
o   b   x   d   o   e   e   m   p   a
m   o   n   e   y   k   s   r   e   l
o   o   k   f   n   i   t   e   n   w
s   k   p   e   n   c   i   l   s   k
a   l   n   o   d   e   i   o   n   y
d   i   c   t   i   o   n   a   r   y
r   y   v   i   m   f   v   s   o   f
w   g   c   i   o   a   e   k   e   i
```

Exercise B   Read the story. Write sentences.

Tomas needs money for school.

He buys lunch for $3.00 on Friday.

He needs to buy three pencils, two pens, and two
notebooks.

He takes the bus to school and back on Monday and
Tuesday. The bus is $1.25 each way.

One Step Up
Write answers in your
notebook.

1. How much money does
   Tomas need this week?
2. What things do you need
   for school?

1. One pencil is 20¢. <u>Three pencils are 60¢.</u>

2. One pen is $2.00. _____

3. One notebook is $3.00. _____

4. One bus ride is $1.25. _____

Exercise C Tomas buys things for school. How much are they?
Write the questions. Answer the questions.

 $2.00 $.20 $3.00   Dictionary $4.95

1. _How much is the pen?_ _____ _The pen is two dollars._ _____

2. _____ _____

3. _____ _____

4. _____ _____

Exercise D Read the story. Circle the correct answer.

Tomas is at school today. He is ready for his class.

Tomas says, "Good morning, Mr. Allen," to his teacher.

Tomas talks to a new student, Amir.

Amir asks, "Where can I buy supplies for school?"

Tomas tells Amir.

1. Tomas is
   a. at the store.
   (b.) at school.
   c. late for school.

2. Tomas calls his teacher
   a. Amir.
   b. teacher.
   c. Mr. Allen.

3. Amir is
   a. a new student.
   b. a teacher.
   c. late for school.

4. Amir needs to
   a. buy school supplies.
   b. be on time.
   c. thank the teacher.

Looking at Your Goals Think about your goals for this unit.

How well can you . . .	Not very well		Somewhat		Very well
tell the month and day?	1	2	3	4	5
talk about the weather?	1	2	3	4	5
talk about transportation?	1	2	3	4	5
follow classroom directions?	1	2	3	4	5
talk about school supplies?	1	2	3	4	5

Learning about Being Ready for School Think about the
three lessons. What was the most important thing you learned
about being ready for school?

_____

_____

Improving Your English In this unit you studied these things.
Check the things that you improved.

_____ using time and weather words

_____ understanding classroom directions

_____ talking about days and months

_____ talking about transportation

_____ talking about school supplies

_____ counting money

_____ recognizing syllable stress

_____ using subject pronouns with *be*

_____ using contractions with *be*

_____ using possessive nouns and adjectives

_____ using plurals of regular nouns

_____ drawing conclusions from a picture

_____ scanning for information on a sign

_____ _____
another thing that you improved

Lesson 1   A Family Problem

Exercise A   Say the words. How many syllables are in the words?
Write the words.

✔apartment	father	job	mother	new	relatives

One Syllable	**Two Syllables**	**Three Syllables**
_____	_____	___apartment___
_____	_____	_____

Exercise B   Unscramble the words. Write the words in the sentences.

country	✔family	home	house	life	neighborhood	relatives

This is a picture of Benita and her _____family_____ *ilfmay*
                                        1

in her old _____ *hogodnborhei.*
               2

This is her mother and father's_____ *soehu.*
                                    3

Benita's _____ *moeh* _____ *nutoryc*
              4   5

is Mexico.

She has many friends and _____ *artiveesl* in Mexico.
                              6

Her new _____ *feli* isn't in Mexico. It's in the US.
             7

Exercise C   Write four sentences about your home country.

1. _____

2. _____

3. _____

4. _____

Exercise D Look at the family tree. Write the names of your relatives in the circles. Write who they are. Use these words.

brother	father	✔grandmother	mother	son
daughter	grandfather	husband	sister	wife

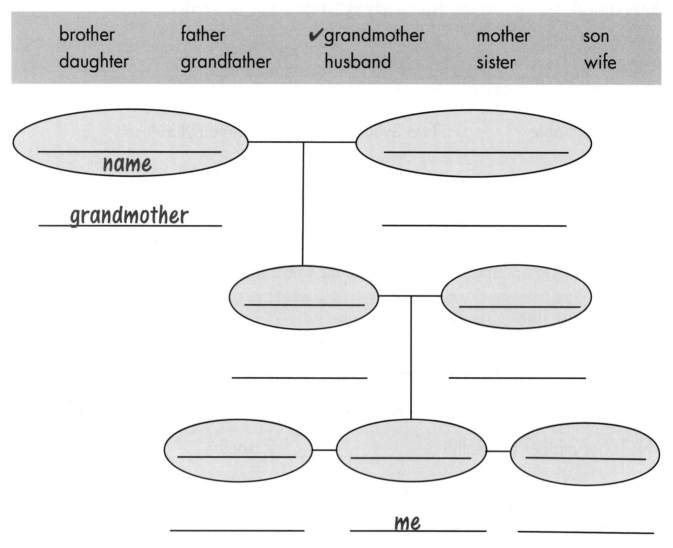

Exercise E Use words from Exercise D to write sentences. Tell who your relatives are.

1. _Inez is my mother._

2. _____

3. _____

4. _____

5. _____

6. _____

Lesson 2 The Neighborhood

Exercise A Write the words in the puzzle.

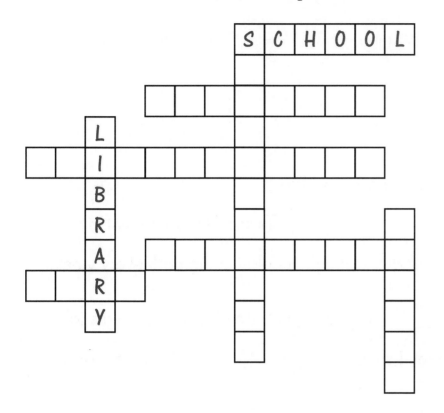

Across
- apartment
- hospital
- neighborhood
- park
- ✔ school

Down
- ✔ library
- street
- supermarket

Exercise B Write each word from Exercise A in a sentence.
Use each word one time.

1. Lusala is a nurse at the _____.

2. Nassim wants to find an _____ with three bedrooms.

3. Nassim and Lusala like the supermarket on their _____.

4. Nassim's daughters go to _____ every day.

5. She likes to get books at the _____.

6. On Saturday, the girls can play in the _____.

7. Nassim likes the places in her _____.

8. She buys things at the _____.

Exercise C Read the letter from Nassim to her mother and father.
Write the words in the sentences.

address	at	change	live	near	on

Dear Mother and Father,

We are ready for you! I'm happy!

We _____ in a new apartment. The _____ is
                1   2

3746 Bay Street. It's a good _____ for us. Our apartment is
                                      3

_____ a park. Your granddaughters play in the park every week.
        4

The apartment is _____ a good street. It's also near Lusala's job
                          5

at the hospital and a supermarket. I shop _____ the supermarket
                                                    6

every week.

Love,
Nassim

Answer the questions.

1. Is Nassim sad? _No, she isn't._ _____

2. Is the apartment on Bay Street? _____

3. Is their apartment near a park? _____

4. Is Lusala's job at the library? _____

5. Is the apartment near a supermarket? _____

Exercise D In your notebook, write a letter to a relative or friend.
Write about your neighborhood in the US.

Lesson 3 Jobs, Jobs, Jobs!

Exercise A Read the ads. Circle the correct answer.

resume to: 555-8675

Restaurant Servers; Hours 5-10 PM, Tues.-Sat. nights. Apply in person on Mondays 1-5 p.m.

Central Hotel Secretary; Computer experience; 1352 Main Street; Full-time. Apply online www.centralhotel.com

...g computer and ...nication... skills needed. Call 555-2345.

River City School Teacher's Aide; No experience necessary. 8-12 noon M-F; English required. Call 555-2876.

Nurses RN's LPN's CNA's needed. Apply now to Central Medical. Send

1. How many nights each week is the restaurant job?
   a. five hours
   b. five nights
   c. 5–10 P.M.
   d. 555-2876

2. When is the school job?
   a. 555-4242
   b. four hours
   c. 8–12 noon
   d. English

3. What do you need for the hotel job?
   a. a secretary
   b. English
   c. a car
   d. computer experience

4. What job is not in the ads?
   a. teacher's aide
   b. server
   c. secretary
   d. teacher

Exercise B What job do you want? Write an ad for the job.
When do you work? What experience do you need?

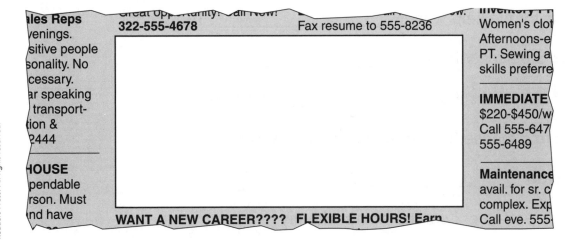

les Reps venings. sitive people sonality. No cessary. ar speaking transport- ion & 2444

Great opp...tunity. Call Now! 322-555-4678

Fax resume to 555-8236

Inventory P... Women's clot... Afternoons-e... PT. Sewing a... skills preferre...

IMMEDIATE $220-$450/w... Call 555-647... 555-6489

HOUSE pendable rson. Must nd have

WANT A NEW CAREER???? FLEXIBLE HOURS! Earn

Maintenance avail. for sr. c... complex. Exp... Call eve. 555-...

Exercise C Write the commands in alphabetical (ABC) order.
Match the command with the rest of the sentence.

Print	✔Call	Spell	Tell	Sign

1. _____Call_____   N-A-S-S-I-M.

2. _____   *Nassim Keino.*

3. _____   Nassim Keino.

4. _____   me your address.

5. _____   555-2354.

One Step Up
In your notebook, write the sentences from Exercise C.

Call 555-2534.

Exercise D Unscramble the sentences.

1. nice / Wear / clothes.   _Wear nice clothes._

2. time. / Be / on   _____

3. hands. / Shake   _____

4. you. / things / Tell / about / good   _____

Exercise E Read. Write the words in the sentences.

application	experience	full-time	job	parents

Nassim: Thanks for the help with my _____ . The school
1

needs a person with my _____ .
2

Lusala: Good for you! Is it a _____ you like?
3

Nassim: Yes! I'm a teacher's aide at our daughters' school!

Lusala: Is the job _____?
4

Nassim: No, it's part-time. I can be home with my _____ a lot.
5

Looking at Your Goals Think about your goals for this unit.

How well can you . . .	Not very well		Somewhat		Very well
talk about your family?	1	2	3	4	5
find places in your neighborhood?	1	2	3	4	5
complete a job application?	1	2	3	4	5
another goal: _____	1	2	3	4	5

Learning about Neighborhood Places and Job Applications

Think about the three lessons. What was the most important thing
you learned about finding places in your neighborhood?

_____

_____

What was the most important thing you learned about completing
a job application?

_____

_____

Improving Your English In this unit you studied these things.
Check the things that you improved.

_____ using family words

_____ using neighborhood words

_____ using job ad words

_____ using negative contractions
with *be*

_____ asking and answering *yes/no*
questions with *be*

_____ using commands

_____ using *in, on, at,* and *near* to find
places

_____ knowing what to say at an
interview

_____ recognizing intonation in
questions and answers

_____ finding the main idea in a story

_____ scanning for information in job ads

Lesson 1 I Need a Favor!

Exercise A   Write the words in alphabetical (ABC) order.

end	_____activity_____
go	_____
✔ activity	_____
work	_____
start	_____
plan	_____
trade	_____
favor	_____
calendar	_____
note	_____

Exercise B   Read the story. Write the correct words in the sentences.

birthday	note	party	schedule	trade	works

Boris _____ at a bakery with Jake.

　　　　　　1

His son, Pavel, wants a party for his _____ .

　　　　　　　　　　　　　　　　　　2

Boris has a problem. He works on Saturday.

Saturday is the day of the _____ .

　　　　　　　　　　　　　3

He needs a change in his _____ .

　　　　　　　　　　　　4

Boris writes a _____ to Jake.

　　　　　　　5

They _____ work days.

　　　　6

Exercise C Circle *Yes* or *No*.

BAKERY NAME	MONDAY	TUESDAY	WEDNESDAY	THURSDAY	FRIDAY	SATURDAY	SUNDAY	
	17	18	19	20	21	22	23	
Boris		8-5	8-5	8-5	8-5	8-5		
Jake	8-5	8-5	8-5	8-5	8-5			

1. Boris and Jake work on Monday. Yes (No)
2. Jake works four days a week. Yes No
3. Jake starts work at 5:00 P.M. on Tuesday. Yes No
4. On Wednesday, Boris starts work at 8:00 A.M. Yes No
5. Boris ends work at 6:00 P.M. on Monday. Yes No
6. Boris and Jake work on Sunday. Yes No

Exercise D What is your schedule this week? Make a chart like the one in Exercise C. Use the chart to write sentences.

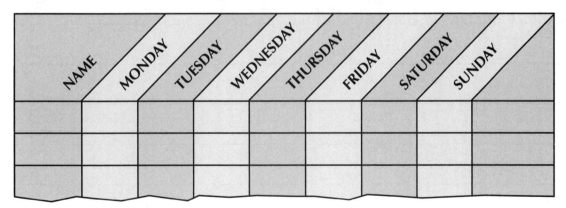

1. ___I work at_____.

2. ___I start work at_____.

3. ___I end work at_____.

In-Class Extension Read your sentences to your partner. Listen to your partner's sentences. Write three sentences about your partner's work.

___Sandra works at ABC Company.___

Lesson 2 Planning the Party

Exercise A   Say the words. What sound does *s* have? Write the words.

✔ balloons	cakes	dates	makes
buys	celebrates	is	meetings

s   **z**

_____   balloons

_____   _____

_____   _____

_____   _____

Exercise B   Write sentences. Use a word from each box.

always	often	sometimes		buy	make	send
never	rarely			celebrate	plan	

1. I sometimes plan a party for my birthday.

2. _____

3. _____

4. _____

5. _____

6. _____

7. _____

8. _____

9. _____

10. _____

Exercise C Unscramble the sentences.

1. send / invitations. / party / sometimes / People

_____

2. and / tell the / date / time / of / Invitations / the party.

_____

3. good / It / on / is / to be / time.

_____

4. buy / for / People / birthday / usually / parties. / presents

_____

5. parties. / at / have / usually / birthday / People / cake

_____

Exercise D Write about yourself. Start your answers with *at, from,* or *on.*

1. What hours do you work? _from 6:30 p.m. to 9:00 p.m._

2. What hours do you go to school? _____

3. What time does your class start? _____

4. What time does your class end? _____

5. Where do you go to school? _____

6. What days do you go to school? _____

7. Where do you talk English with friends? _____

Lesson 3 Changing Plans!

Exercise A Say the words. What sound does *a* have? Write the words.

activity	date	Jack	make	plan
ask	glad	Jake	place	trade

take   **class**

_____   _____

_____   _____

_____   _____

_____   _____

_____   _____

Exercise B Circle the correct answer.

1. Do Pavel's parents meet Ben's parents?
   a. Yes, he does.
   b. Yes, they do.
   c. Yes, they are.
   d. Yes, they don't.

2. _____ Pavel thank Ben for his present?
   a. Do
   b. Does
   c. Do they
   d. Are

3. _____ Miguel and Sylvia Ben's parents?
   a. Is
   b. Do
   c. Are
   d. Does

4. Does Sylvia need to call Boris next week?
   a. Yes, she is.
   b. Yes, she does.
   c. Yes, they do.
   d. Yes, he do.

Exercise C Read the story.

A Great Day!

It's 6:00 P.M. on Saturday. It's sunny now.
Boris and Yelena thank Jack and Rosa for their help.
They laugh about the rain.
A change in plans can be fun, too!

Yelena and Boris are glad that they know
Pavel's friends.
Pavel likes his presents.
Boris is happy that Ben's mother needs a cake.
What a great day!

Answer the questions.

1. Do Boris and Jack thank Yelena and Rosa?

   No, they don't.

2. Does the rain end?

   _____

3. Do they have fun?

   _____

Write the question.

4. Yes, he likes his presents.

   Does Pavel like his presents?

5. Yes, she needs a cake.

   _____

Looking at Your Goals   Think about your goals for this unit.

How well can you . . .	Not very well		Somewhat		Very well
write a note?	1	2	3	4	5
change a work schedule?	1	2	3	4	5
invite people to an activity?	1	2	3	4	5
plan an activity?	1	2	3	4	5
plan for changes?	1	2	3	4	5
another goal: _____	1	2	3	4	5

Learning about Planning an Activity   Think about the three
lessons. What was the most important thing you learned about
planning an activity?

_____

_____

Improving Your English   In this unit you studied these things.
Check the things that you improved.

_____ using planning words

_____ using work schedule words

_____ using present tense

_____ asking *yes/no* questions

_____ answering *yes/no* questions

_____ finding details in a story

_____ saying two sounds of *a*

_____ saying ending sounds of present-tense verbs

_____ telling what time you do something

_____ telling how often you do something

_____ reading work schedules

_____ listening for cause and effect

_____ _____
                another thing that you improved

Lesson 1 Sick at Work

Exercise A   Is it an illness or a symptom? Is it a medicine? Write the words.

✔allergies	cold	cough syrup	flu	sore throat
aspirin	cough drops	fever	headache	stomachache

Illness	Symptom	Medicine
allergies	_____	_____
_____	_____	_____
_____	_____	_____
	_____	

Exercise B   Write the words in the puzzle.

S I C K

W
E L L
L

Across

feel
medical
✔sick
stay
symptom

Down

give
illness
take
✔well

Exercise C   Read the note. Write the correct words in the sentences.

cough	her	it	sick	them	you

From the Desk of Jim Morgan

Dear Mrs. Ramirez,

I'm _____ . I need to go home. I have a bad _____ .
         1   2

I don't want to give _____ to anyone at work. I'm sorry I have to
                                   3

miss the meeting. Call Mr. and Mrs. Mankin. Tell _____ to call
                                                          4

me on Wednesday. Mary has their phone number. Please get it from

_____ . I'll call _____ tomorrow and tell you
       5   6

how I feel.

Exercise D   Complete the questions with the words from the box.
Answer the questions using *it* or *them*.

✔ aspirin	cough drops	cough syrup	tissues

1. Do you have _____ _aspirin_ _____ at home?

   Yes, I have it at home.

2. Do you have _____ at home?

   _____

3. Do you have _____ at home?

   _____

4. Do you have _____ at home?

   _____

Lesson 2 Making a Doctor's Appointment

Exercise A Look at Jim's appointment card. Read the questions.
Answer the questions.

```
┌─────────────────────────────────────────────┐
│            Dr. Patrick Lee, MD                │
│   241 Central Avenue, San Francisco, CA 94119 │
│               (415) 555-2275                  │
│                                               │
│  Appointment for: Jim Martin                  │
│  Monday (Tuesday) Wednesday  Thursday  Friday │
│  Date: June 10                                │
│  Time: 3:00                    a.m. (p.m.)    │
└─────────────────────────────────────────────┘
```

1. Who is Jim's doctor?   Jim's doctor is Dr. Lee.

2. What day is his appointment? _____

3. What time is his appointment? _____

4. Where is Dr. Lee's office? _____

Exercise B Write questions. Use a question word and a verb.

✔How	Why	When		✔are	is	is

1. I'm sick.

____How____ ____are____ you?

2. The office is open from 8:30 A.M. to 4:00 P.M.

_____ _____ the office open?

3. Jim has a fever.

_____ _____ Jim hot?

Exercise C Read the conversation. Circle *True* or *False*.

Jim: Hello, Dr. Lee.

Dr. Lee: Good afternoon. How are you today?

Jim: Not very well. My throat's sore, and I feel hot.

Dr. Lee: Well, you have a fever. Your temperature is 101°.
I want to see your throat. Do you have a stomachache?

Jim: No, my stomach's OK. But I have a headache.

Dr. Lee: You need medicine. Take aspirin for the fever. Then
stay home and rest.

1. Dr. Lee is sick.   True   (False)

2. Jim is sick.   True   False

3. Jim doesn't have a fever.   True   False

4. Jim has a stomachache and a headache.   True   False

5. Jim needs medicine.   True   False

Exercise D Match the words from the left column to the words
in the right column.

_c_ **1.** allergies   a. Dr. Smith

____ **2.** symptom   b. 9:00 A.M. – 5:00 P.M.

____ **3.** fever   c. sneeze

____ **4.** appointment   d. sore throat

____ **5.** doctor   e. 101°

____ **6.** office open   f. Wednesday at 2:00 P.M.

Lesson 3 Take Your Medicine!

Exercise A Write the words on the medicine label.

Daily Maximum	✔Dose	Expiration Date	Warning

Tummy Ease

For a Stomachache

_____Dose_____   Take 2 to 4 tablets as needed.

_____   16 tablets

_____   Do not use maximum dose for more
                            than 2 weeks.

_____   Nov/2008

Exercise B Complete each question with *do* or *does*.

> as needed = when you need it
> daily = in a day

1. Why _____do_____ you take aspirin?
   For pain.

2. What _____ cough drops help?
   Sore throat and cough.

3. Where _____ Jim have his medicine?
   In his medicine cabinet.

4. How often _____ adults take cough syrup?
   Every four hours.

5. When _____ Jim take cough drops?
   Every hour.

6. Who _____ you ask questions about medicine?
   Your doctor.

Exercise C Read the label. Circle the correct answer.

1. Who is this medicine for?
   a. all children and adults
   b. 12 children
   c. adults and children 12 years and over
   d. adults only

2. What is the expiration date?
   a. February 2060
   b. February 2006
   c. February 6
   d. February 20

3. How much medicine can you take in one day?
   a. 4 hours
   b. 8 teaspoons
   c. 4 teaspoons
   d. 2 teaspoons

4. When do you take this medicine?
   a. every 2 hours
   b. every 4 hours
   c. every 8 hours
   d. every 12 hours

Exercise D Unscramble the words. Write the correct words in the sentences.

| directions | drugstore | pain | remedy | tablets |

Jim goes to the _____ *oresdrgut* to get medicine. He reads the
     1

_____ *tinsrideoc*. When he gets home, he takes two aspirin
     2

_____ *bealtts* to relieve the _____ *inap*. He also
     3   4

drinks hot tea. Tea is his favorite home _____ *medyer*.
                                              5

Looking at Your Goals Think about your goals for this unit.

How well can you . . .	Not very well		Somewhat		Very well
make a doctor's appointment?	1	2	3	4	5
call in sick to work or school?	1	2	3	4	5
complete a medical information form?	1	2	3	4	5
read a medicine label?	1	2	3	4	5
ask questions with *who, what, when, where, why?*	1	2	3	4	5
talk about illnesses and symptoms?	1	2	3	4	5
another goal: _____	1	2	3	4	5

Learning about Getting Medical Help Think about the three lessons. What was the most important thing you learned about getting medical help?

_____

_____

Improving Your English In this unit you studied these things. Check the things that you improved.

_____ talking about illness and symptoms

_____ talking about home remedies

_____ using question words

_____ reading medicine labels

_____ using object pronouns

_____ asking present-tense *Wh-* questions with *be*

_____ asking present-tense *Wh-* questions with other verbs

_____ _____
another thing that you improved

Lesson 1 Thinking about Saving Money

Exercise A Find these words. Look across ➔ and down ↓.
Circle the words. Write the words in your notebook.

| cheap | check | e-mail | rent | save | spending | thinking | trying |

s	p	e	n	d	i	n	g
b	e	k	t	p	c	w	t
r	f	l	h	r	h	c	d
e	m	a	i	l	e	h	s
n	g	m	n	e	a	e	a
t	h	h	k	w	p	c	v
t	r	y	i	n	g	k	e
c	j	n	n	q	r	s	h
c	k	o	g	y	y	a	k

Exercise B Write all the words from Exercise A in the sentences.
Use each word one time.

1. Ramon is _____trying_____ to _____ money.

2. He needs to write a _____ for his _____.

3. Are you _____ a lot of money on movies?

4. This computer is not expensive. It's _____.

5. I need a computer to _____ my friends.

6. Are you _____ about a new job?

Exercise C Write about your budget. Do you need to save more money?
Write sentences in your notebook.

Exercise D Read the ad for long-distance phone service.
Then circle *True* or *False*.

MOUNTAIN VALLEY
has a phone plan for you!
Pay $5.95 a month and only 7 cents a minute day and night for calls in the US.
Calls to Mexico are only 15 cents a minute.
Call 555-9352 today and get this plan!

1. The plan costs $15.95 each month.   True   False

2. You pay 7 cents a minute for calls in the US.   True   False

3. You pay 51 cents a minute for calls to Mexico.   True   False

4. You can call 555-9352 to get the plan.   True   False

Exercise E Read the conversation between Ramon and his classmate Ken.
Write the correct words in the sentences.

checks	credit card	expenses	money	pay	think

Ken: Hi, Ramon. How are you? You don't look happy.

Ramon: I'm not. I need more _____ . I have a lot of bills.
                                              1

Ken: I have a lot of bills too. I'm using my _____ too much. I'm
                                                          2

trying to write _____ or _____ with cash now.
                        3   4

Ramon: That's good.

Ken: Do you have a roommate? A roommate helps with _____ .
                                                                           5

Ramon: That's true! Do you have a roommate?

Ken: No. Let's _____ about being roommates.
                              6

Lesson 2 Improving Your Job Skills

Exercise A Say the words. What sound does *e* have? Write the words.

be	cheap	check	credit	end	pencil	see	speak

need   **rent**

_____   _____

_____   _____

_____   _____

_____   _____

Exercise B Answer the questions for you.

1. What do you want to do better?

   <u>I want to speak English better.</u>_____

2. What do you need to practice?

   _____

3. When do you need to be at school?

   _____

4. Why do you want to go to school?

   _____

In-Class Extension Ask your partner the questions in Exercise B. Write the answers in your notebook.

   <u>Maria wants to write English better.</u>_____

34 *Unit 4 Lesson 2*

Exercise C Unscramble the sentences and questions.

1. more / Ramon / at work. / wants to / have / hours

   _____

2. needs to / his / service. / Ramon / improve

   _____

3. Does / work? / need to / speak more / Ramon / English / at

   _____

4. a lot of / spend / Does / rent? / for / money / need to / Ken

   _____

5. apartment. / Ken / and / want to / an / rent / Ramon

   _____

Exercise D Write the letter of the correct answer to each question.

_d_ **1.** Do you need to practice English more?

_____ **2.** How do you save money?

_____ **3.** Are you worried about money?

_____ **4.** Where do you need to speak English?

a. I need to speak it at work.

b. Yes, my bills are very expensive.

c. I have a roommate.

d. No, I speak it every day.

Write the questions and answers in your notebook.

Do you need to practice English more?   No, I speak it every day.

Lesson 3 Shopping for Clothes

Exercise A Unscramble the words. Write the sentence using *this*, *that*, *these*, or *those*.

| clothes | fit | ✔shirts | shoes | sweater |

1. _____ **ssirth** are too tight.

   <u>These shirts are too tight.</u>

2. I want to return _____ **sseoh.** They don't **itf.**

   _____

3. Is _____ **setarew** on sale?

   _____

4. Do you need _____ **sehtcol** for work?

   _____

Exercise B Ramon wants to buy clothes. Write two lists. What clothes does Ramon need for work? What clothes does he need for home?

long pants   shoes   shorts   sweater   white shirt   loose T-shirt

Clothes for Work   **Clothes for Home**

<u>long pants</u>   _____

_____   _____

_____   _____

36 *Unit 4 Lesson 3*

Exercise C Change the underlined words. Write the new sentences.

3 for $ 39

1. Ramon wants a <u>shirt</u>.

Ramon wants a sweater.

2. Ken wants to try on <u>clothes</u>.

_____

3. The shirts on sale are <u>2 for $33</u>.

_____

4. Ramon needs to return a pair of <u>shorts</u>.

_____

Exercise D Read the conversation. Write the correct words in the sentences.

this	that	these	those	pants	service	shirt	trying

Ramon: Do you want to talk to me, Mr. Martin?

Mr. Martin: Yes, _____ customers are smiling
                                     1

_____ time.
           2

Ramon: I'm really _____ ! My _____ is better.
                                   3   4

Mr. Martin: And you are doing a very good job! Is _____ a new
                                                                        5

_____?
         6

Ramon: Yes, I want to look nice for work, so I'm also wearing

_____ new _____ . Now, I get big tips
           7   8

from my customers!

Looking at Your Goals Think about your goals for this unit.

How well can you . . .	Not very well		Somewhat		Very well
learn ways to save money?	1	2	3	4	5
make a budget?	1	2	3	4	5
talk about things you want, need, and like?	1	2	3	4	5
return something you buy?	1	2	3	4	5
another goal: _____	1	2	3	4	5

Learning about Making a Budget Think about the three lessons. What did you learn about making a budget?

_____

_____

Improving Your English In this unit you studied these things.
Check the things that you improved.

____ talking about money

____ using job skill words

____ talking about clothes

____ using the present continuous tense

____ reading a journal

____ using *need, need to, want, want to, like, like to*

____ finding information in ads

____ using *this, that, these, those*

____ saying long and short *e* sounds

____ listening to a conversation

____ _____
another thing that you improved

Lesson 1 At the Supermarket

Exercise A Write the correct words in the sentences.

aisle	are not	corn	is not	produce
are	bakery	dairy	meat	

1. _____ is in aisle 11 in the produce section.

2. Cookies are in the _____ section in aisle 6.

3. Bacon is in the _____ section in _____ 3.

4. Apples _____ in the produce section in aisle 11.

5. Milk is in the _____ section in aisle 7.

6. Cookies _____ in the dairy section in aisle 7.

7. Bananas are in the _____ section.

8. Butter _____ in the produce section.

Exercise B Is it produce, dairy, or meat? Write the words.

apples	butter	chicken	milk	tomatoes
bananas	cheese	lettuce	steak	yogurt

Produce	**Dairy**	**Meat**
_____	_____	_____
_____	_____	_____
_____	_____	
_____		

Exercise C   Read the story. Answer the questions.

Miyako needs to go to the supermarket. She writes the foods she needs.

She needs eggs and milk for breakfast. She also needs fish, yogurt, lettuce, and soup. She wants to have chicken for dinner tonight. Chicken is on sale today.

Sometimes Miyako cannot find the foods. She often asks the clerk where the foods are.

1. Where does Miyako need to go?   _She needs to go to the supermarket._

   _____

2. What food does she need? _____

   _____

3. When does she want to have chicken? _____

   _____

4. What is on sale today? _____

   _____

5. Who does she ask where the foods are? _____

   _____

Exercise D   Think about your meals. What time do you eat?
What do you like to eat for breakfast, lunch, dinner, and a snack?
Write sentences in your notebook.

   I eat breakfast at 6:00 a.m. I like to eat rice and eggs for breakfast.

Lesson 2 Saving Money on Food

Exercise A Underline the syllable that has the stress. Write the word.

1. to ma to _____
2. break fast _____
3. cook ies _____
4. ba na nas _____
5. ex pen sive _____

6. noo dles _____
7. news pa per _____
8. but ter _____
9. let tuce _____
10. po ta toes _____

Exercise B Match the words to make sentences.

1. There is   expiration dates on the coupons for yogurt.
2. There are   food coupons for cereal in this magazine?
3. There is   corn on sale at Sam's Market?
4. There are   a food coupon for potatoes in the newspaper.
5. Is there   good savings on fruit.
6. Are there   a special on rice today.

Write the sentences.

  <u>There is a food coupon for potatoes in the newspaper.</u>

_____

_____

_____

_____

_____

Exercise C   Read the coupons. Circle the correct answer.

Price Beaters
Special

Chicken **$1.79** a lb.
Regular Price **$3.89** a lb.

Save-a-Lot

Bananas **$1.39** a lb.
Buy one lb., get one free!

Super-Mart

Bananas **99¢** a lb.

Chicken Soup **4 cans for $1**

Sam's Market

Apples **$1.99** a lb.
Eggs **$2.19** a dozen

1. What store has cheap soup?
   a. Super-Mart
   b. Save-a-Lot
   c. Price Beaters
   d. Sam's Market

2. What kind of produce is on sale at Sam's Market?
   a. chicken
   b. eggs
   c. bananas
   d. apples

3. Where is chicken on sale?
   a. Save-a-Lot
   b. Sam's Market
   c. Price Beaters
   d. Super-Mart

4. How much can you save on chicken at Price Beaters?
   a. $2.79 a lb.
   b. $3.89 a lb.
   c. $2.10 a lb.
   d. $4.79 a lb.

Exercise D   In your notebook, make your own coupon. What store do you use? What food do you like? How much do you want to save? Is there an expiration date or limit?

Lesson 3 It's Lunch Time!

Exercise A Write the words in the puzzle.

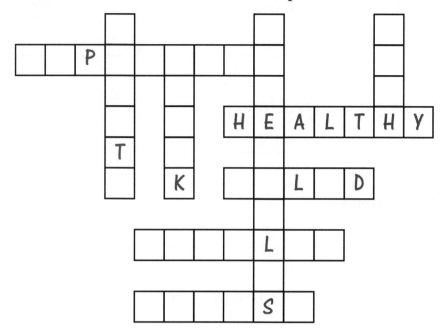

Across

choose
expensive
✔healthy
popular
salad

Down

fish
health
snack
vegetables

Exercise B Pizza is a popular fast food in the US. Think of foods to put on pizza. Write the foods under produce, dairy, or meat. Write sentences about your pizza.

Produce	Dairy	Meat
_____	_____	_____
_____	_____	_____
_____	_____	_____
_____	_____	_____

1. I like _____*sausage*_____ or _____ on my pizza.

2. I like _____ and _____ on my pizza.

3. I like _____

4. _____

Exercise C Unscramble the sentences.

1. order / Many / for / people / fast food / dinner.

   _____

2. is / food / popular / Fast / people. / busy / for

   _____

3. They / have / to cook. / time / don't

   _____

4. Some / food / restaurants / deliver / people's homes. / to

   _____

Exercise D Read the conversation between Miyako and her husband.
Write the correct words in the sentences.

| burgers | cheap | eat out | fries | meal | unhealthy |

Miyako: I'm worried about the _____ *yuneahhtl* food that
 1

our children eat.

Hiro: I agree that they don't need cookies, sodas,

_____ *ubsgrre,* and _____ *serif.*
2 3

Miyako: And they want to eat out often. It's not _____ *phcae!*
 4

Hiro: I like to _____ *tae tou* with the family. We sit together
5

and talk during the _____ *lame.* And there are no
6

phone calls or TV. I think that it's OK one day a week!

Looking at Your Goals Think about your goals for this unit.

How well can you ...	Not very well		Somewhat		Very well
plan meals?	1	2	3	4	5
eat healthy food?	1	2	3	4	5
save money on food?	1	2	3	4	5
make healthy meals that your family likes?	1	2	3	4	5
ask for foods at restaurants and stores?	1	2	3	4	5
another goal: _____	1	2	3	4	5

Learning about Buying Food Think about the three lessons.
What was the most important thing you learned about buying food?

_____

_____

Improving Your English In this unit you studied these things.
Check the things that you improved.

_____ using food words

_____ reading coupons

_____ saying words in a list

_____ ordering food at a restaurant

_____ listening to a conversation

_____ reading charts

_____ using count and noncount nouns

_____ using *there is* and *there are*

_____ asking and answering questions with *or*

_____ _____
        another thing that you improved

Lesson 1 What a Mess!

Exercise A Say the words. What sound does *i* have? Write the words.

bike	fish	important	light	rice	window

tight   **it**

_____   _____

_____   _____

_____   _____

Exercise B Circle the correct answer.

1. Where was Sara Wednesday night?
   a. She was at work.
   b. She is at work.
   c. She works on Tuesday.
   d. It was Tuesday.

2. Was Sara going home?
   a. No, she isn't.
   b. No, he wasn't.
   c. Yes, it was.
   d. Yes, she was.

3. Was it late?
   a. Yes, it was early.
   b. Yes, it was.
   c. It was Wednesday.
   d. No, it isn't.

4. What is Sara's job?
   a. Yes, she was.
   b. He's a teacher.
   c. She's a nurse.
   d. No, she isn't.

Exercise C Put the story in order. Number the sentences 1 to 5.
Write the story in your notebook.

_____ Sara was not happy when she got home.

_____ She needed to call the police!

__1__ It was Wednesday night.

_____ The apartment was a mess. The TV and VCR were gone.

_____ Her apartment door was open!

Exercise D Look at the two pictures. Find these things.

bookcase	chair	computer	table	sofa	TV	VCR

8:00 P.M.   10:00 P.M.

List three things that are not in the same place. Tell where
they were.

1. _____TV_____   __A TV was in the bookcase._____

2. _____   _____

3. _____   _____

4. _____   _____

Lesson 2 Talking to the Police

Exercise A Say the words. What sound does the past-tense ending have?
Write the words.

arrived	happened	liked	protected	walked	wanted

worked   **played**   **waited**

_____   _____   _____

_____   _____   _____

Exercise B Read the conversation. Write the correct words in the sentences.

arrived	crime report	happened	TV	witness
computer	fill out	mess	VCR	

Officer Collins: Ms. Morgan, we need you to _____ a

  _____ . Please tell us what _____ .
  ₂   ₃

Sara: I came home about 10:00 P.M. When I _____ at
  ₄

  my apartment, the door was open. I went inside, looked around,

  and I saw this _____ !
  ₅

Officer Collins: What did the burglar take?

Sara: Several things—a _____ , a
  ₆

  _____ , and a _____ .
  ₇   ₈

Officer Collins: Did your neighbors see anything?

Sara: Yes, my neighbor, Mrs. Caruso, was a _____ . She
  ₉

  saw a man outside with a TV at about 9:50 P.M.

Exercise C Read the question and the answer. Write the verb.

1. What did you see last night?   I _____*saw*_____ a man outside.

2. What did he wear?   He _____ a dark shirt.

3. What did he have?   He _____ a TV.

4. Where did he take it?   He _____ it to his van.

5. Where did he go?   He _____ on that street.

6. Who did you call?   I _____ the police.

7. When did they arrive?   They _____ at 10:00 P.M.

Exercise D Complete the chart.

Do you have a:	Yes/No	Where did you get it?	When did you get it?
car?	Yes	Lodi Automall	1999
TV?			
computer?			
VCR?			
radio?			

Write sentences for you.

1.   I got my car at the Lodi Automall in 1999.

2. _____

3. _____

4. _____

5. _____

Lesson 3 Wanted!

Exercise A Write the letter of the correct answer to each question.

_____ **1.** Did Sam have black hair?

_____ **2.** Were his eyes blue?

_____ **3.** Was Boris tall?

_____ **4.** Was Sara thin?

_____ **5.** Did Antonio and Ramon have mustaches?

_____ **6.** Did it rain last night?

_____ **7.** Was it hot last night?

_____ **8.** Did the suspect wear glasses?

_____ **9.** Did Sara see the suspect?

_____ **10.** Did you wear glasses?

a. No, she didn't.

b. Yes, I did.

c. Yes, they were.

d. No, they didn't.

e. Yes, she was.

f. No, it wasn't.

g. Yes, he did.

h. Yes, he was.

i. No, it didn't.

j. No, he didn't.

Exercise B Draw a picture of a friend or relative in your home country.
Write sentences about him or her.

My friend was Juanita.

She had black hair.

_____

_____

_____

_____

In-Class Extension Show the picture to your class. Read your sentences to the class.

Exercise C Unscramble the sentences. Write questions.

1. call / the / night? / last / police / you / Did

   _____

2. burglar / have / a beard / mustache? / the / Did / or

   _____

3. give / a / Did / to / you / description / the police?

   _____

Exercise D Read the conversation. Write the correct words in the sentences.

have	light	locked	stopped	van	were

Officer Collins: Hi, Sara, this is Officer Collins. We _____
                                                                    1

your things.

Sara: That's great! Where _____ they?
                                      2

Officer Collins: A police officer _____ a _____ . All
                                              3   4

your things were in there.

Sara: Thank you so much!

Officer Collins: Is your apartment safe now?

Sara: Yes. This morning I turned on a _____ . And I
                                                  5

_____ all the doors.
          6

Looking at Your Goals Think about your goals for this unit.

How well can you . . .	Not very well		Somewhat		Very well
talk to the police?	1	2	3	4	5
report what happened?	1	2	3	4	5
fill out a form?	1	2	3	4	5
talk about protecting your things?	1	2	3	4	5
describe someone?	1	2	3	4	5
another goal: _____	1	2	3	4	5

Learning about Reporting a Crime Think about the three lessons.

What was the most important thing you learned about reporting a crime?

_____

_____

Improving Your English In this unit you studied these things.

Check the things that you improved.

_____ using home safety words

_____ talking about things in your house

_____ giving descriptions of people

_____ reading descriptions of people

_____ using police report words

_____ pronouncing past-tense endings

_____ pronouncing short and long
       i sounds

_____ using the past tense of *be*

_____ using the past tense of regular
       verbs

_____ using the past tense of irregular
       verbs

_____ asking questions in the past

_____ _____
               another thing that you improved

Lesson 1 Reading a Report Card

Exercise A Look at Ruby's and Justin's schedules. Read the questions.
Answer the questions.

Class Schedule for		Bortin, Ruby
Period	**Class**	**Teacher**
1	P.E.	Mr. Taylor
2	US History	Ms. Jones
3	Math	Ms. Vegas
4	English	Mr. Lo
5	Spanish	Mrs. Hart
6	Computer	Ms. Schultz

Class Schedule for		Brown, Justin
Period	**Class**	**Teacher**
1	Computer	Ms. Strong
2	US History	Ms. Jones
3	Spanish	Mrs. Hart
4	P.E.	Mr. Taylor
5	English	Mr. Lo
6	Math	Ms. Vegas

1. Who is Justin's math teacher?

His math teacher is Ms. Vegas.

2. Who is Ruby's P.E. teacher?

_____

3. Who is Justin's and Ruby's US history teacher?

_____

4. Who is Ruby's Spanish teacher?

_____

5. Who is Justin's and Ruby's English teacher?

_____

Exercise B Circle the correct answer.

Karl

Erick

Thuy

Julie

Minh

Tuyen

1. Thuy is **the children's** mother.
   a. She is our mother.
   b. She is her mother.
   c. She is their mother.
   d. She is his mother.

2. Erick and Tuyen are **Minh's** brothers.
   a. They are his brothers.
   b. They are your brothers.
   c. They are their brothers.
   d. They are her brothers.

3. Thuy is **Karl's** wife.
   a. She is her wife.
   b. She is his wife.
   c. She is their wife.
   d. She is your wife.

4. This is a picture of the Jones family. Do you have a picture of **your** family?
   a. Yes, I have a picture of his family.
   b. Yes, I have a picture of your family.
   c. Yes, I have a picture of her family.
   d. Yes, I have a picture of my family.

Exercise C Write the words in the puzzle.

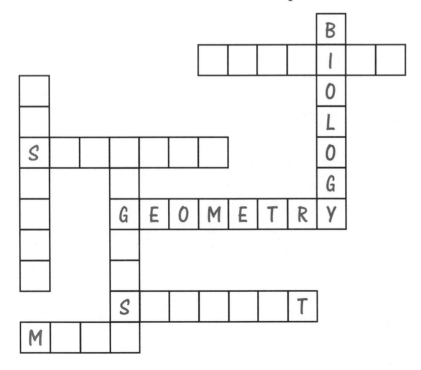

Across

✔ geometry
math
science
Spanish
subject

Down

✔ biology
English
history

Lesson 2 Making Decisions

Exercise A Think about last Saturday. What did you do at these times?
Write sentences.

1. 8:00 A.M.–10:00 A.M.

   I ate breakfast and read the newspaper.

2. 10:00 A.M.–12:00 noon

_____

3. 12:00 noon–2:00 P.M.

_____

4. 2:00 P.M.–4:00 P.M.

_____

5. 4:00 P.M.–6:00 P.M.

_____

6. 6:00 P.M.–8:00 P.M.

_____

Exercise B Say the words. What sound does *o* have? Write the words.

hello	job	okay	phone	shop
home	lot	on	piano	soccer

go   **not**

_____   _____

_____   _____

_____   _____

_____   _____

_____   _____

Exercise C Unscramble the sentences.

1. practices / Minh / piano / Tuesday. / the / on

   _____

2. like? / sports / does / Minh / What

   _____

3. and / basketball. / likes / Minh / soccer

   _____

4. She / brothers / helps / at home. / her / and sisters

   _____

5. busy. / Minh / very / is

   _____

Lesson 3 Parent-Teacher Meeting

Exercise A What's going to happen? Write the letter of the sentence that tells what happens next.

_b_ **1.** Minh is going to study Sunday night.

____ **2.** Mr. Albers wants to talk to Minh's mother.

____ **3.** Minh is often late with her homework.

____ **4.** Thuy is worried about Minh's grades.

____ **5.** Minh is thinking about going to summer school.

a. Thuy is going to check Minh's homework.

b. She has a geometry exam Monday morning.

c. Thuy is going to talk to Minh about changes in Minh's life.

d. He is going to have a meeting with Thuy after school.

e. Thuy is going to call the principal's office for a summer school schedule.

Exercise B How are you going to improve your work at school?
Use the pictures to write about you or your children.

1. I'm not going to watch TV late at night. _____

2. _____

3. _____

4. _____

5. _____

Exercise C Read the conversation. Write the correct words in the sentences.

check	fail	meeting	pass	succeed	teacher

Thuy: Minh, I talked to your _____ today. We had a

1

_____ after school.

2

Minh: What did he say?

Thuy: He is worried about your schoolwork. I don't want you to

_____ his class. We need to make changes.

3

Minh: I know. I am very busy this year.

Thuy: You need more time to study. You need to _____ your

4

classes. School is very important.

Minh: I enjoy all my activities, but there are too many for me. I need to

quit my job until the summer.

Thuy: You're right. I'm going to _____ your homework

5

every day. And I'm going to try to change my work schedule.

Then you can sleep until 7:00 A.M. in the morning.

Minh: Thanks, Mom. I want to be a good student again.

I want to _____ .

6

In-Class Extension Read the conversation with a partner. Talk about what
happens next.

Looking at Your Goals Think about your goals for this unit.

How well can you . . .	Not very well		Somewhat		Very well
talk to your child's teacher?	1	2	3	4	5
talk to your teacher?	1	2	3	4	5
go to a school meeting?	1	2	3	4	5
read a report card?	1	2	3	4	5
decide what things in your life are important?	1	2	3	4	5
change your schedule?	1	2	3	4	5
another goal: _____	1	2	3	4	5

Learning about Succeeding in School Think about the three lessons.

What was the most important thing you learned about succeeding in school?

_____

_____

Improving Your English In this unit you studied these things.

Check the things that you improved.

_____ using school words

_____ making compound sentences with *and*

_____ talking about after-school activities

_____ using future tense with *going to*

_____ using possessive adjectives

_____ saying long and short *o* sounds

_____ reading report cards and schedules

_____ listening to a conversation

_____ reading about a parent-teacher meeting

_____ _____
another thing that you improved

Lesson 1 Good For You!

Exercise A   Write the words in the puzzle.

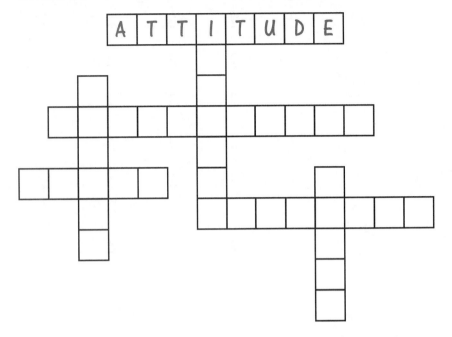

Across

✔attitude
employee
performance
skill

Down

improve
review
solve

Exercise B   Read the story. Write the correct words in the sentences.

| congratulates | GED | promotion | responsibility |
| diploma | helps | qualified | supervisor |

Ms. Hunter is Cesar's _____. She _____ him
                              1   2

for being Employee of the Month. Cesar is on time every day,

and he always _____ his co-workers.
                       3

Ms. Hunter wants to give Cesar a _____. She thinks he can
                                              4

get a better job. It gives him more _____ and better pay. But
                                              5

Cesar needs his high school _____ or a _____ to
                                    6   7

be _____ for that job.
        8

Exercise C
Use the chart to rate yourself as a student. In your notebook, write four sentences about your skills. Write about things you *can* do and *can't* do.

Student Performance Review

School Name:

Student: | | Class:

STUDENT SKILLS	Excellent	Good	Fair	Needs to Improve
On time	☐	☐	☐	☐
At school every day	☐	☐	☐	☐
Attitude	☐	☐	☐	☐
Class participation	☐	☐	☐	☐
Completes work on time	☐	☐	☐	☐

Exercise D
Read the conversation. Write *can* or *can't* to complete the sentences.

Ms. Hunter: Cesar! _____ Can _____ you talk to me for a minute?

1

Cesar: Yes, I _____ .

2

Ms. Hunter: Good. I want you to apply for the supervisor job. You

_____ get an application in the office.

3

Cesar: I _____ apply yet. I have one more GED Test to take.

4

Ms. Hunter: When _____ you take it?

5

Cesar: I work during the days and some nights. I _____ take

6

another class.

Ms. Hunter: Let's talk more later. We _____ solve this problem.

7

Lesson 2 Planning a Future

Exercise A Read the story. Write the correct words in the sentences.

apply	deserves	library	responsible
comments	diploma	positive	supervisor

Pilar works at the _____. She does not get money for her work,
                        1

but she gets experience. Her _____ likes her good work and
                              2

always has _____ _____ for Pilar. Pilar always
            3   4

arrives on time, and she is _____. She has a high school
                            5

_____. Pilar wants to _____ for a job with pay at the
6   7

library. She _____ the job!
             8

Exercise B What do these workers need? Write sentences.

1. He wants a promotion, but

_he talks too much on the job_____.

2. She wants to apply for a job with more money, but

_____.

3. He wants a raise, but

_____.

Exercise C Write sentences about Daren and Amina using *like to*.

1. _Daren likes to watch TV, but Amina_
likes to read books.
_____

2. _____
_____
_____

3. _____
_____
_____

Think about a relative or friend. What do each of you like to do
at home, work, and school? In your notebook, write three sentences
about you. Write three sentences about your relative or friend.

In-Class Extension Talk to your partner. What do you like to do at home, work,
and school? In the circles, write the things you and your partner like. Then write
the things you both like.

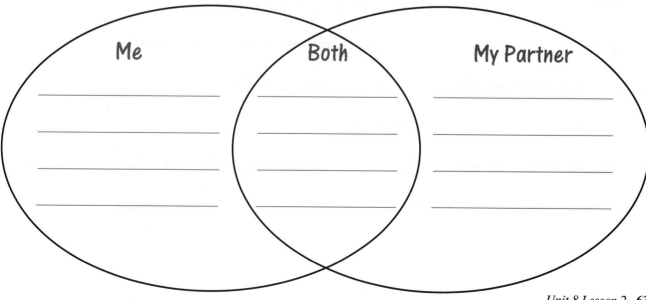

Me   Both   My Partner

Lesson 3 Distance Learning

Exercise A Unscramble the sentences.

1. and / see / for / flyers / distance-learning / Cesar / classes. / Pilar

   _____

2. can / take / They / at home. / distance-learning / a / class

   _____

3. ESL / take / They / GED / and / can / classes.

   _____

4. on / a class / They / can / or / the / take / Internet. / on TV

   _____

5. videos / check out / Pilar / ESL / can / library. / the / at

   _____

Exercise B Write *a, an,* or *the* to complete the sentences.

1. People in _____the_____ US can get _____ job

   with _____ high school diploma.

2. But _____ education often means more income.

3. Some people take distance-learning classes on TV

   or on _____ Internet.

4. People who work during _____ day can sometimes take

   _____ class at night.

Exercise C Read the flyers. Circle *Yes* or *No*.

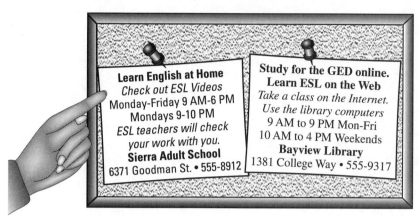

Learn English at Home
Check out ESL Videos
Monday-Friday 9 AM-6 PM
Mondays 9-10 PM
ESL teachers will check your work with you.
Sierra Adult School
6371 Goodman St. • 555-8912

Study for the GED online.
Learn ESL on the Web
Take a class on the Internet.
Use the library computers
9 AM to 9 PM Mon-Fri
10 AM to 4 PM Weekends
Bayview Library
1381 College Way • 555-9317

1. You can call 555-8912 to learn about videos.   Yes   No
2. You can check out a video on Friday at 8:00 P.M.   Yes   No
3. Sierra Adult School is on Goodman Street.   Yes   No
4. You can study for the GED online.   Yes   No

Exercise D Pilar and Cesar are calling about the distance-learning programs. Read their conversations. Unscramble the words. Write the correct words in the sentences.

check out	GED	Internet	online	video	Web

Pilar: Hello, this is Pilar Cortez. I saw a flyer about your video

_____ *cckeh tou* program on the bulletin board at the
           1

library. Can you send me a registration form? How often can

the teacher check my work? I can come in tomorrow to get

my first _____ *evdio.*
               2

Cesar: Hi, this is Cesar Rios. I need more information about the

_____ *elinno* _____ *DGE* class on the
           3   4

_____ *tnntelre.* I'm going to come into the library
           5

next week. Can I use a computer in the afternoons? Can I get

on the _____ *beW?*
                6

Looking at Your Goals Think about your goals for this unit.

How well can you . . .	Not very well		Somewhat		Very well
understand a job performance review?	1	2	3	4	5
talk to your supervisor about job opportunities?	1	2	3	4	5
talk to your teacher about your ESL progress?	1	2	3	4	5
make choices about your job?	1	2	3	4	5
register for other education or training programs?	1	2	3	4	5
another goal: _____	1	2	3	4	5

Learning about Improving Your Skills Think about the
three lessons. What did you learn about improving your skills?

_____

_____

Improving Your English In this unit you studied these things.
Check the things that you improved.

____ using employment words

____ using *a, an,* and *the*

____ talking about opportunities for more school

____ pronouncing long and short *u* sounds

____ understanding performance reviews

____ using *can* and *can't*

____ reading a story about jobs

____ listening to a conversation about the future

____ reading flyers for specific information

Grammar Talk: Subject Pronouns with *Be*

Subject Pronoun	Verb *Be*	(Contraction)		Subject Pronoun	Verb *Be*	(Contraction)	
I	**am**	(I**'m**)	a student.	**He**	**is**	(He**'s**)	a teacher.
You	**are**	(You**'re**)	Tomas.	**She**	**is**	(She**'s**)	lost.
We	**are**	(We**'re**)	students.	**It**	**is**	(It**'s**)	sunny.
They	**are**	(They**'re**)	late.				

What letters are missing in the contractions? Write the letters with your teacher.

Grammar Talk: Possessive Nouns and Adjectives

Tomas	Tomas**'s**	Tomas's phone number is 916-555-1928.
Maria	Maria**'s**	Maria's address is 5876 Hillside Road.
the teacher	the teacher**'s**	The teacher's name is Mr. Allen.

What changes in the words Tomas, Maria, *and* teacher?

I	**my**	Check **my** answers.	we	**our**	Check **our** numbers.
you	**your**	Spell **your** name.	you	**your**	Write **your** answers.
he	**his**	Answer **his** question.	they	**their**	Read **their** words.
she	**her**	Read **her** answer.			

Grammar Talk: Plurals of Regular Nouns | Using *Need* and *Need To*

I need a **book.**	I need two **books.**	I **need** $3.00.
The **pen** is blue.	The **pens** are blue.	I **need to** pay $3.00.

Most nouns add s for plurals: book ⟶ books

What kind of word follows need?
What follows need to?
Talk to your teacher.

Grammar Talk: Negative Contractions with *Be*

I am not	I'm not		his brother.
You are not	You're not	You aren't	his sister.
He is not	He's not	He isn't	from the US.
She is not	She's not	She isn't	from Kenya.
It is not	It's not	It isn't	from Mexico.
We are not	We're not	We aren't	in New York.
You are not	You're not	You aren't	brothers.
They are not	They're not	They aren't	sisters.

What are the missing letters in the contractions? Talk about this question with your teacher.

Grammar Talk: Yes/No Questions and Answers with *Be*

	Question with *Be*	Short Answer
Nassim is in her apartment.	**Is Nassim** in her apartment?	Yes, she **is**.
Jamie and Samantha *are* at school.	**Are they** at the park?	No, they **aren't**.

Where is the verb be *in questions? Where is* be *in short answers?*

Grammar Talk: Commands

Sign your name.	**Circle** the letter.
Call 555-4242.	**Spell** your last name.
Print your information.	**Tell** me your phone number.

Commands tell you to do something. Use the base form of verbs in commands.

Grammar Talk: Present-Tense Verbs

Subject	Verb		Subject	do + not	(Contraction)	Verb
I	need	help.	I	do not	(don't)	need help.
You	work	today.	You	do not	(don't)	work today.
We	trade	days.	We	do not	(don't)	trade days.
They	write	notes.	They	do not	(don't)	write notes.
He	wan**ts**	a party.	He	does not	(doesn't)	want a party.
She	work**s**	at home.	She	does not	(doesn't)	work at home.
It	end**s**	at 5:00.	It	does not	(doesn't)	end at 5:00.

Some verbs have different forms.

I **have** (don't have) to work.   She **has** (doesn't have) to work.

I **go** (don't go) to school on Friday. He **goes** (doesn't go) to school on Friday.

What words make a verb negative? Talk with your teacher.

Grammar Talk: Present Tense Yes/No Questions and Answers

Question		Yes Answer	No Answer	(Contractions)
Do	I need to call?	Yes, you **do.**	No, you **do not**	(don't).
Do	we like parties?	Yes, we **do.**	No, we **do not**	(don't).
Do	they see balloons?	Yes, they **do.**	No, they **do not**	(don't).
Does	he like his presents?	Yes, he **does.**	No, he **does not**	(doesn't).
Does	she eat some cake?	Yes, she **does.**	No, she **does not**	(doesn't).
Does	it rain at the party?	Yes, it **does.**	No, it **does not**	(doesn't).

What is the first word in the question? What is the last word in the Yes answer? What is the last word in the No answer? Talk to your teacher about these questions.

Grammar Talk: Object Pronouns

Aspirin helps **me** feel better.
The doctor can see **you** tomorrow.
Can you take **him** home?
Call **her** at work.
Buy **it** at the drugstore.
Can you see **us** today?
Can you take **them**?
Tanya gives **a cough drop** to **Jim**. She gives **it** to **him**.

Where do object pronouns go in a sentence? Talk to your teacher.

Grammar Talk: Present-Tense *Wh-* Questions with *Be*

		(Contraction)		
Why	**am**		I hot?	You have a fever.
How	**are**		your children?	They're sick.
Where	**is**	(Where's)	the aspirin?	It's in the cabinet.
Who	**is**	(Who's)	your doctor?	He's Dr. Ramos.
When	**is**	(When's)	your appointment?	It's tomorrow.
What	**is**	(What's)	your temperature?	It's 101°.

Where is the question word? What form of be *is in contractions? What letter is missing in the contraction?*

Grammar Talk: Present-Tense *Wh-* Questions with Other Verbs

How	*do*	I take this medicine?	Read the directions.
When	*do*	you see the doctor?	I see him tomorrow.
What	*do*	we need at the store?	You need cough syrup.
Why	*do*	they need aspirin?	They have headaches.
Where	*does*	Dr. Lee work?	He works at the clinic.
Who	*does*	Jim call?	He calls his boss.

Where is the question word? What word comes after the question word?

Grammar Talk: Present Continuous Statements and Questions

Subject	Be	(Contraction)	
I	**am**	(I'**m**)	buy**ing** clothes for work.
You	**are**	(You'**re**)	tak**ing** an English class.
He	**is**	(He'**s**)	liv**ing** with two friends.
She	**is**	(She'**s**)	study**ing** English.
We	**are**	(We'**re**)	try**ing** to save money.
You	**are**	(You'**re**)	work**ing** a lot of hours.
They	**are**	(They'**re**)	plann**ing** to register for class.

Questions			
	He	**is**	work**ing.**
	Is	he	work**ing** at the store now? Yes, he **is.**
Where	**is**	he	work**ing**? at the store

What ending do you add to the main verb to make the present continuous? Talk about the answer to this question with your teacher.

Grammar Talk:
Like and *Like To*, *Need* and *Need To*, *Want* and *Want To*

Ramon **likes his job.**	He **likes to work** at the restaurant.
Ramon **needs more hours** at work.	He **needs to ask** his boss.
The customers **want good service.**	They **want to talk** to their waiter now.

What follows want, need, *and* like? *What verb form follows* want to, need to, *and* like to? *Talk about the answers to these questions with your teacher.*

Grammar Talk: *This, That, These, Those*

I need to	return	**this**	blue shirt.
I want to	see	**that**	coat.
I need to	try on	**these**	sweaters.
I want to	buy	**those**	black shoes.

What words do you use for things near you? What words do you use for things not near you? Talk to your teacher about these questions.

Grammar Talk: Count and Noncount Nouns

Count Nouns	Noncount Nouns
Apples are in the produce section.	**Chicken is** in the meat section.
Cookies are not in the produce section.	**Corn is** not in the meat section.
Tomatoes are on sale.	**Milk is** in aisle 7.

Count nouns *name things you can count, like apples.* Noncount nouns *name things you cannot count, like chicken. What verb is used with* apples? *With* chicken?

Grammar Talk: *There Is* and *There Are*

There is a special today.	
Is there a special today?	<u>Yes</u>, **there is.**
There is a food coupon in the magazine.	
Is there a food coupon in your apartment?	<u>No</u>, **there isn't.**
There are food coupons in magazines in the US.	
Are there food coupons in magazines in your country?	<u>Yes</u>, **there are.**
There are food coupons in the newspaper.	
Are there food coupons in the phone book?	<u>No</u>, **there aren't.**

Use there is *with singular nouns. Use* there are *with plural nouns.*

Grammar Talk: Questions and Answers with *Or*

Do you eat lunch at home **or** at work?
I eat lunch at work.

Where do you buy your food?
I buy it at Happy Mart **or** at Smart Shop.

Use or *to talk about choices.*

Grammar Talk: Past-Tense Statements with *Be*

Subject	Verb		Subject	Verb + *not*	(Contraction)	
I	**was**	at school.	I	**was not**	**(wasn't)**	at work.
He/She	**was**	at work.	He/She	**was not**	**(wasn't)**	at school.
It	**was**	rainy.	It	**was not**	**(wasn't)**	sunny.
You/We	**were**	at home.	You/We	**were not**	**(weren't)**	at the store.
The dishes	**were**	expensive.	They	**were not**	**(weren't)**	cheap.

What word makes the verb negative? What letter is missing in the contraction?

Grammar Talk: Past-Tense Statements with Regular and Irregular Verbs

Regular Verbs			Negative = did not	(didn't)	
I	work**ed.**	I	**did not**	**(didn't)**	work.
He/She	wait**ed.**	He/She	**did not**	**(didn't)**	wait.
You	play**ed.**	You	**did not**	**(didn't)**	play.
We/They	studi**ed.**	We/They	**did not**	**(didn't)**	study.

Regular verbs use -ed to show past tense. Irregular verbs do not.

I **do** my homework every day.	I **did** my homework last night.
Mrs. Caruso often **sees** Sara.	Mrs. Caruso **saw** the burglar.
I **have** my photos in an album now.	I **had** my photos in a box before.
She **goes** home at 10:00 every night.	She **went** home at 10:00 last night.
We always **take** our lunch to work.	We **took** our lunch to work Friday.
He **wears** blue jeans most days.	He **wore** black pants yesterday.

Grammar Talk: Past-tense Questions with *Be and Other Verbs*

Question Word	Verb	Subject		Answer
	Were	you	at home last night?	Yes, I was.
Where	**were**	you	last night?	I was at home.

Question Word	Helping Verb	Subject		Main Verb Answer
	Did	you	**lock** the door?	No, I did not. (didn't)
When	**did**	you	**call** the police?	I called them last night.

Grammar Talk: Possessive Adjectives (Review)

Subject Pronoun	Possessive Adjective	
I	my	I like **my** new teacher.
you	your	**You** can open **your** book now.
he, she, it	his, her, its	**She** does **her** homework every night.
we	our	**We** have **our** class picnic on Friday.
you	your	Do **you** have **your** English book?
they	their	**They** have **their** lunch at noon.

Minh's basketball game is on Friday. = **Her** basketball game is on Friday.

What follows a possessive adjective? What does a possessive adjective tell you?

Grammar Talk: Compound Sentences with *And*

Thuy starts work at 6:00 A.M. Minh starts school at 8:00 A.M.

Thuy starts work at 6:00 A.M.**, and** Minh starts school at 8:00 A.M.

Thuy gets home at 5:00 P.M. Minh gets home at 8:00 P.M.

Thuy gets home at 5:00 P.M.**, and** Minh gets home at 8:00 P.M.

What word makes two sentences into one sentence? What do you see before the word and *in these sentences?*

Grammar Talk: Future Tense with *Going to*

Subject	Be	Going to	Main Verb (Base Form)	
I	**am**	**going to**	check	my daughter's homework.
You	**are**	**going to**	call	the principal.
He/She	**is**	**going to**	talk	to Minh.
We/They	**are**	**going to**	meet	with the counselor.

What verb comes before going to*? What verb* form *follows* going to*?*
Remember: To make a question with a form of be, *put it in front of the subject.*
   Thuy is *going to talk to Minh.*   Is *Thuy going to talk to Minh?*

Grammar Talk: *Can* and *Can't*

Statement			Question	
I	**can/can't** apply for the job.		**Can/Can't**	I apply for the job?
You	**can/can't** solve the problem.		**Can/Can't**	you solve the problem
He/she	**can/can't** speak English		**Can/Can't**	he/she speak English?
We	**can/can't** do the job.		**Can/Can't**	we do the job?
They	**can/can't** succeed.		**Can/Can't**	they succeed?

Can and can't *let you talk about things you have the ability to do.*
What kind of word follows can *or* can't *in a statement? What word changes place in a question? Talk to your teacher about these questions.*

Grammar Talk: Compound Sentences With *But*

Cesar wants a supervisor job, **but** he needs a high school diploma.

He likes his company, **but** he wants a different job there.

What punctuation mark is used before but? *Talk to your teacher.*

Grammar Talk: *A, An, The*

I want to check out **a** video.   I'm going to take **an** Internet course.

Do you need **an** ESL video?   Yes, I need **the** video for **the** first three lessons.

What letter follows a? *What letter follows* an?
Use a *and* an *with one person, place, or thing.*
Use the *with one or more people, places, or things.*
A or an *refers to any singular item. The* refers to a specific item or items.*

Warm-Up Unit

address
answer
April
area code
ask
August
book
buy
change
city
class
clerk
cloudy
day
December
dictionary
dime
dollar
drive a car
early
February
five dollars
Friday
half dollar
How much?
information
January
July
June
late
listen
March
May
Monday
money
month
name
nickel
notebook
November

October
on time
open
paper
pen
pencil
penny
phone
quarter
rainy
raise (your hand)
ready
ride a bike
Saturday
September
spell
state
student
Sunday
sunny
supplies
take a bus
take a train
talk
teacher
tell
ten dollars
Thursday
Tuesday
twenty dollars
walk
Wednesday
write
zip code

Unit 1

ad
apartment
application
at
brother

call
change
children
circle
country
daughter
education
experience
family
family tree
father
full-time
grandfather
grandmother
grandparents
home
hospital
house
husband
interview
job
library
life
like
live
mother
near
neighborhood
new
now
old
on
parents
park
part-time
print
relatives
school
sign
sister
son

street
supermarket
wife

Unit 2

A.M.
activity
always
balloons
birthday
cake
calendar
celebrate
date
eat
end
favor
friend
glad
go
great
guest
happy
help
invitation
invite
list
make
meeting
never
note
often
P.M.
party
place
plan
present
rarely
schedule
see
send

sometimes
start
take
thank you
thanks
there
trade
work

Unit 3

allergies
appointment
aspirin
cold
cough
cough drops
cough syrup
directions
doctor
dose
drugstore
expiration
feel
fever
flu
give
headache
how
hurt
illness
label
maximum
medical
medicine
office
pain
remedy
sick
sneeze
sore throat
stay

stomachache
symptom
tablet
teaspoonful (tsp.)
temperature
tissue
warning
well
what
when
where
who
why

Unit 4

better
bill
budget
cheap
check
clothes
credit card
dress
e-mail
expenses
expensive
fit
improve
long
loose
on sale
pants
pay
phone
practice
rent
restaurant
return
sale
save
service
shirt

shoes
short
speak
spend
sweater
tight
too much
try
try on
T-shirt
utilities
wear

Unit 5

apples
bakery
bananas
bread
breakfast
butter
cereal
cheese
chicken
choice
choose
cook
cookies
corn
coupon
dairy
deliver
dinner
eat out
eggs
fast food
fish
for here
french fries (fries)
fruit
groceries
hamburgers
    (burgers)

health
healthy
hungry
lettuce
lunch
magazine
meal
meat
milk
newspaper
noodles
popular
potatoes
produce
rice
salad
savings
soup
snack
steak
to go
tomatoes
unhealthy
vegetables
worried
yogurt

Unit 6

arrive
beard
burglar
burglary
computer
crime
dark
describe
description
door
glasses
happen
heavy
important

inside
insurance
key
light
lock
locked
mess
mustache
outside
photo album
police
protect
quiet
radio
replace
report
safe
short
strange
tall
thin
TV
van
VCR
window
witness

Unit 7

basketball
busy
check
counselor
English
fail
history
homework
math (geometry)
pass
physical
    education (P.E.)
piano
principal

science (biology)
soccer
Spanish
sports
study
subject
succeed
tired
work

Unit 8

apply
cable TV
check out
comment
congratulate
congratulations
deserve
distance learning
employee
GED
high school
    diploma
Internet
negative
online
opportunity
performance
positive
promote
promotion
qualified
responsibility
responsible
review
skill
solve
supervisor
tape
video
web

Answer Key

Warm-up Unit
Lesson 1

Exercise A
2. Monday   5. Thursday
3. Tuesday   6. Friday
4. Wednesday   7. Saturday

Exercise B
2. a   3. d   4. c   5. b

Exercise C
2. are   3. are   4. am   5. is

Exercise D
2. It's cloudy on Wednesday.
3. It's rainy on Thursday and Friday.

Exercise E
2. It's   3. cloudy   4. on time

Lesson 2

Exercise A
2. sup <u>plies</u>   5. <u>o</u> pen
3. <u>rain</u> y   6. <u>Mon</u> day
4. <u>an</u> swer

Exercise B
2. His   3. Their   4. Her

Exercise D

```
            B
 W R I T E  E
 A     T E L L
 A S   A     I
 S P E L L   S
 K     K     T
       D     E
       O P E N
```

Exercise E
2. Raise   5. Talk   8. Tell
3. Open   6. Listen   9. Spell
4. Write   7. Do   10. Be

Lesson 3

Exercise A

Exercise B
2. Two pens are $4.00.
3. Two notebooks are $6.00.
4. Four bus rides are $5.00.

One Step Up
1. $18.60

Exercise C
2. How much is the pencil?
   The pencil is twenty cents.
3. How much is the notebook?
   The notebook is three dollars.
4. How much is the dictionary?
   The dictionary is four dollars and
   ninety-five cents.

Exercise D
2. c   3. a   4. a

Unit 1
Lesson 1

Exercise A
One Syllable - job, new
Two Syllables - father, mother
Three Syllables - relatives

Exercise B
2. neighborhood   5. country
3. house   6. relatives
4. home   7. life

Lesson 2

Exercise A

```
              S C H O O L
              U
        H O S P I T A L
        L     E
 N E I G H B O R H O O D
        B     M         S
        R     A         T
        A P A R T M E N T
 P A R K      K         R
        Y     E         E
              T         E
                        T
```

Exercise B
1. hospital   5. library
2. apartment   6. park
3. street   7. neighborhood
4. school   8. supermarket

Exercise C
1. live   4. near
2. address   5. on
3. change   6. at

2. Yes, it is.   4. No, it isn't.
3. Yes, it is.   5. Yes, it is.

Lesson 3

Exercise A
1. b   2. c   3. d   4. d

Exercise C
2. Print Nassim Keino.
3. Sign *Nassim Keino.*
4. Spell N-A-S-S-I-M.
5. Tell me your address.

Exercise D
2. Be on time.   4. Tell good things
3. Shake hands.   about you.

Exercise E
1. application   4. full-time
2. experience   5. parents
3. job

Unit 2
Lesson 1

Exercise A
calendar, end, favor, go, note, plan, start, trade, work

Exercise B
1. works   3. party   5. note
2. birthday   4. schedule   6. trade

Exercise C
2. No   3. No   4. Yes   5. No   6. No

Lesson 2

Exercise A
s - cakes, celebrates, dates, makes
z - buys, is, meetings

Exercise C
1. People sometimes send party
   invitations.
2. Invitations tell the date and time,
   (or time and date) of the party.
3. It is good to be on time.
4. People usually buy presents for
   birthday parties.
5. People usually have cake at birthday
   parties.

Lesson 3

Exercise A
take - date, Jake, make, place, trade
class - activity, ask, glad, Jack, plan

Exercise B
1. b   2. b   3. c   4. b

Exercise C
2. Yes, it does.
3. Yes, they do.
5. Does Ben's mother need a cake?

Answer Key

Unit 3
Lesson 1

Exercise A
Illness - cold, flu
Symptom - fever, headache, sore throat, stomachache
Medicine - aspirin, cough drops, cough syrup

Exercise B

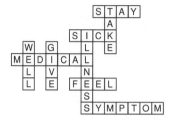

Exercise C
1. sick   3. it   5. her
2. cough   4. them   6. you

Lesson 2

Exercise A
2. His appointment is Tuesday, June 10.
3. His appointment is at 3:00 P.M.
4. His office is at 241 Central Avenue.

Exercise B
2. When is   3. Why is

Exercise C
2. True   3. False   4. False   5. True

Exercise D
2. d   4. f   6. b
3. e   5. a

Lesson 3

Exercise A
2. Daily Maximum
3. Warning
4. Expiration Date

Exercise B
2. do   3. does   4. do   5. does   6. do

Exercise C
1. c   2. b   3. b   4. b

Exercise D
1. drugstore   3. tablets   5. remedy
2. directions   4. pain

Unit 4
Lesson 1

Exercise A

Exercise B
1. save   4. cheap
2. check, rent   5. e-mail
3. spending   6. thinking

Exercise D
1. False   2. True   3. False   4. True

Exercise E
1. money   4. pay
2. credit card   5. expenses
3. checks   6. think

Lesson 2

Exercise A
need - be, cheap, see, speak
rent - check, credit, end, pencil

Exercise C
1. Ramon wants to have more hours at work.
2. Ramon needs to improve his service.
3. Does Ramón need to speak more English at work?
4. Does Ken need to spend a lot of money for rent?
5. Ken and Ramon want to rent an apartment.

Exercise D
2. c   3. b   4. a

Lesson 3

Exercise A
2. I want to return these shoes. They don't fit.
3. Is that sweater on sale?
4. Do you need these clothes for work?

Exercise B
Clothes for Work - sweater, white shirt
Clothes for Home - shoes, shorts, loose T-shirt

Exercise C
2. Ken wants to try on shoes.
3. The shirts on sale are 3 for $39.
4. Ramon needs to return a pair of pants.

Exercise D
1. those   4. service   7. these
2. this   5. that   8. pants
3. trying   6. shirt

Unit 5
Lesson 1

Exercise A
1. Corn   5. dairy
2. bakery   6. are not
3. meat, aisle   7. produce
4. are   8. is not

Exercise B
Produce - apples, bananas, lettuce, tomatoes
Dairy - butter, cheese, milk, yogurt
Meat - chicken, steak

Exercise C
2. She needs eggs, milk, fish, yogurt, lettuce, soup, and chicken.
3. She wants to have it for dinner tonight.
4. Chicken is on sale.
5. She asks the clerk where the foods are.

Lesson 2

Exercise A
1. to <u>ma</u> to   6. <u>noo</u> dles
2. <u>break</u> fast   7. <u>news</u> pa per
3. <u>cook</u> ies   8. <u>but</u> ter
4. ba <u>na</u> nas   9. <u>let</u> tuce
5. ex <u>pen</u> sive   10. po <u>ta</u> toes

Exercise B
2. There are expiration dates on the coupons for yogurt.
3. There is a special on rice today.
4. There are good savings on fruit.
5. Is there corn on sale at Sam's Market?
6. Are there food coupons for cereal in this magazine?

Exercise C
1. a   2. d   3. c   4. c

Answer Key

Lesson 3

Exercise A

Exercise C
1. Many people order fast food for dinner.
2. Fast food is popular for busy people.
3. They don't have time to cook.
4. Some restaurants deliver food to people's homes.

Exercise D
1. unhealthy   4. cheap
2. burgers   5. eat out
3. fries   6. meal

Unit 6
Lesson 1

Exercise A
tight - bike, light, rice
it - fish, important, window

Exercise B
1. a   2. d   3. b   4. c

Exercise C
2, 5, 1, 4, 3

Lesson 2

Exercise A
worked - liked, walked
played - arrived, happened
waited - protected, wanted

Exercise B
1. fill out
2. crime report
3. happened
4. arrived
5. mess
6., 7., 8. computer, TV, VCR
9. witness

Exercise C
2. wore   4. took   6. called
3. had   5. went   7. arrived

Lesson 3

Exercise A
1. j   4. e   7. f   10. b
2. c   5. d   8. g
3. h   6. i   9. a

Exercise C
1. Did you call the police last night?
2. Did the burglar have a beard or mustache?
3. Did you give a description to the police?

Exercise D
1. have   3. stopped   5. light
2. were   4. van   6. locked

Unit 7
Lesson 1

Exercise A
2. Her P.E. teacher is Mr. Taylor.
3. Their US history teacher is Ms. Jones.
4. Her Spanish teacher is Mrs. Hart.
5. Their English teacher is Mr. Lo.

Exercise B
1. c   2. d   3. b   4. d

Exercise C

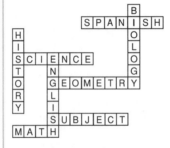

Lesson 2

Exercise B
go - hello, home, okay, phone, piano
not - job, lot, on, shop, soccer

Exercise C
1. Minh practices the piano on Tuesday.
2. What sports does Minh like?
3. Minh likes soccer and basketball.
4. She helps her brothers and sisters at home.
5. Minh is very busy.

Lesson 3

Exercise A
2. d   3. a   4. c   5. e

Exercise C
1. teacher   4. pass
2. meeting   5. check
3. fail   6. succeed

Unit 8
Lesson 1

Exercise A

Exercise B
1. supervisor   5. responsibility
2. congratulates   6. diploma
3. helps   7. GED
4. promotion   8. qualified

Exercise D
2. can   4. can't   6. can't
3. can   5. can   7. can

Lesson 2

Exercise A
1. library   5. responsible
2. supervisor   6. diploma
3. positive   7. apply
4. comments   8. deserves

Lesson 3

Exercise A
1. Cesar and Pilar see flyers for distance-learning classes.
2. They can take a distance-learning class at home.
3. They can take ESL and GED classes.
4. They can take a class on TV or on the Internet.
5. Pilar can check out ESL videos at the library.

Exercise B
1. a, a   2. an   3. the   4. the, a

Exercise C
1. Yes   2. No   3. Yes   4. Yes

Exercise D
1. check out   4. GED
2. video   5. Internet
3. online   6. Web